Adventures in Cartooning

ACTIVITY BOOK

James Sturm
Andrew Arnold
Alexis Frederick-Frost

SCHOLASTIC INC.
New York Toronto London Auckland
Sydney Mexico City New Delhi Hong Kong

Ugh, rain is SO boring.
It's RUINING my life!
Poof
What? Who?!
It's me, the Magical Car-tooning Elf! Why so glum, chum?
Elf!
I'm bored out of my MIND! There's nothing fun to do.

Because of the storm, my play date was cancelled!
Oh, dear!
I've seen all of my DVDs like **A MILLION** times!
And the storm has knocked out our satellite— our TV doesn't work!
CLICK
CLICK
I can't even play my video games because my parents took them away. (I knew I should have cleaned my room!)
This is the **WORST** day of my life, Elf... All is woe!
No, it's not!
You don't need play dates, DVDs, TV, or video games to have fun!
I don't?
NO! All you need is...

Pencil and paper!
Check it out—cool doodles, huh?

I like those doodles but I want something EXCITING.
How about a monster? Or an evil wizard?! Or a GIANT?!!
Let's draw them!

DRAW HERE!

That was fun, Elf, but I want some ACTION...
...and ADVENTURE!
Yes!
I want to battle a monster, a wizard, and a giant!!!
YIKES!
If it wasn't raining, I could go search for them.
Guess what? You CAN do all that!
But how? All we've done is doodle!
Here, I'll show you!
COOL!

See this doodle of a monster? You can take it on an adventure using COMICS. Comics are made of a bunch of picture boxes called PANELS. Each panel shows a moment in time.
When you put the doodles of the monster into panels, the monster jumps over the hole!
Now YOU try! Show the knight jumping over the hole. How HIGH can the knight jump?

That was cool, Elf!
I've got to show this comic to my horse, Edward.
Edward? Hello?
He's not in his room...
...or brushing his teeth...
...and he's not playing ping-pong...
Have you seen Edward?
MISSING!
EDWARD, the horse

Psst!
The knight hasn't checked the dining room table yet. Draw Edward by the table.

There you are, Edward. You're as thin as a rail!
When was the last time you had something to eat?
I wonder where the chef is? He usually feeds you right away.
We've got to get you to food—and fast!!!
Almost...
there...
MADE IT!

Edward loves to eat!
Fill the fridge with yummy foods for him to munch on!

Gosh, Edward, watching you eat has made me hungry.
Me, too!
There's got to be something in this kitchen for us!
COOKIES
Wait a sec... What's that smell? It smells sweet and chocolatey, just like—
CHOCOLATE CHIP COOKIES!
My favorite!
CHOMP!
HEY!
It can talk!

Can you turn THESE cookies into faces?
Add eyes, a nose, ears, and a mouth!
EYES
NOSES
MOUTHS
EARS

That hurt!
YEAH!
How would you like it if we took a bite out of you?!
LET'S GO!
ROAR!
OH, NO! A cookie monster!

The monster is growing larger by the second. The panels show him growing over time. How big does he get? You decide, and draw him in the last panel.

EEK! That's the biggest monster I've ever seen!
C'mon— let's get out of here!!!
RAWR!
FASTER!

Draw Edward and the knight escaping the Cookie Monster. To show how fast they are going, add motion lines or little puffs of dirt!

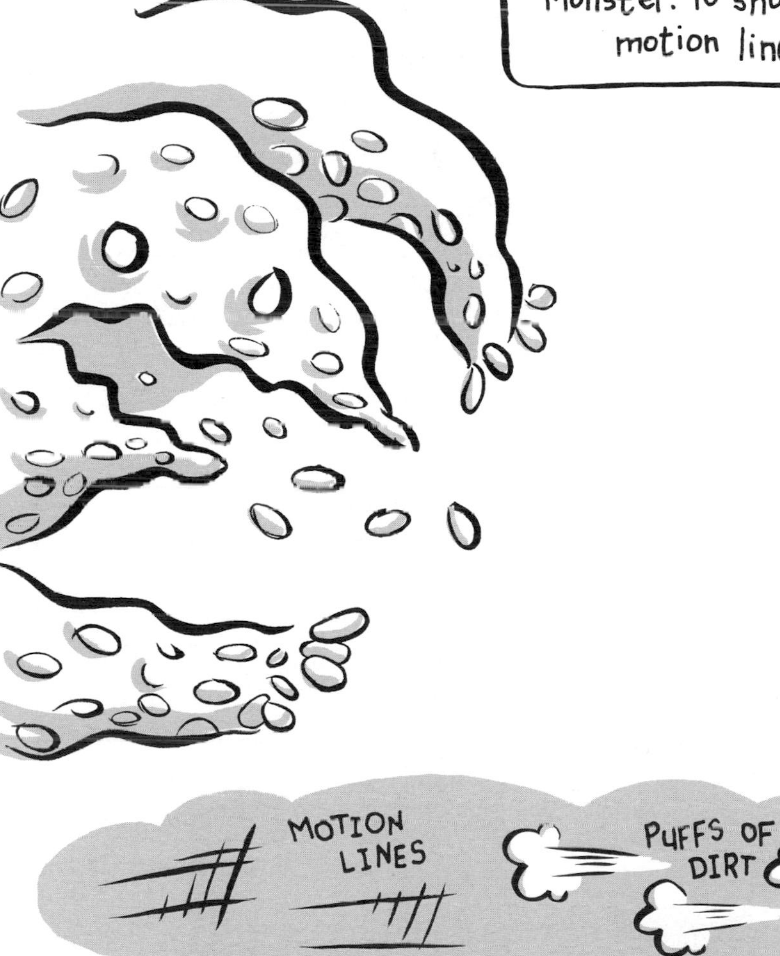

ACK!
I CAN'T SEE!
AAAAHH!
FLOUR
FLOUR
PUFF
Look—COUGH—a carton of milk—COUGH, COUGH!
MILK
And the flour has made you look like a cow, Edward!
Hah!

What else can you turn Edward into?
A unicorn?
A zebra?
A sheep?

That gives me an idea— C'mere, Edward.
?
Back to your cookie jar, monster, or I'll pour milk over you so you become soggy and mushy. I've got a carton of milk and a cow and I'm not afraid to use them!
MOO!
NOT THAT! Please don't dunk me!
Then go!
OK. We are going!
HURRY!
WHOOSH!
COOKIES
VICTORY!
MOO

The knight is excited because he defeated the Cookie Monster.
HOORAY!
What is the knight saying?

YOWZA! What now— An evil wizard?!
POOF!
I'm not an evil wizard — I'm the Magic Chef!
You're the chef?
Yes. I've been hiding from the Cookie Monster. How can I thank you for getting rid of it?
Can you use your magic to stop the rain?
Sadly, my magic is only good for making snacks.
But you were able to defeat the monster, so maybe YOU can stop the rain.
But how?
Try the library. That's where I go when I need information.
Bye, now!

Add a: POOF!

Add a: BANG!

Add a: CRACK!

Some chef... A **CARROT?!** That's the worst chef I've ever met!!!
sniff
Why don't we go to the library like the Magic chef said...?
Hmmm...
Okay, you're right — maybe there will be something useful in there.
munch
munch
LET'S GO!
Burp
Wait—do you hear that? What's that noise?
I dunno.
It sounds like a jack-hammer!
It's coming from the library.

The knight and Edward wonder what is making all the noise in the library. Draw their ideas in their thought bubbles.

SNORE!
I know what it is! It's a SNORE!
huff
SNO
It's the loudest snore I've ever heard.
Me, too!
RE! SNOR
What could possibly snore that loud?!
SNORE! huff huff SNORE huff, huff SNORE! huff
That!
WHOA— A giant!!!

The giant is sleeping soundly in his recliner. Draw the rest of the giant here.
MODEL SHEET

Wow, the GIANT'S library! I wonder if the giant would let me read one of his books? What do you think?
I THINK these books are too big for us, Elf.
GIANTS NEED FRIENDS, TOO
HEAD in the Clouds
THE HUNGRY TROLL
MONSTER
GIANTS in Love
STINKY FEET
How to be the Best Giant
CREATURES AND CAVES
PEOPLE VS. GIANTS

Draw the covers to some of the giant's books!

Shhhh... Be very quiet—the last thing we want to do is wake the giant!
Wait—what's this?
DR. TIN and the
A COMIC BOOK!
Uh-oh!

DR. TINKERTON and the ROBOT
YIKES!
Got it!
Be careful, Elf!
DR. TINKERTON and the ROBOT
Hey, this comic doesn't make any sense!

Comics need to be read from left to right, top to bottom.*
On the next page, redraw these panels in the right order so they make sense.
* Except for Japanese comics!
"Build me a tower—A tower so tall that it disappears into the clouds and rain above!"
Yes, master.
OH, NO! I forgot to ask them to build a door!
Drats!
And so, the robots were stuck in the tower... Forever.
Hello?
END
Once upon a time...
I've done it!
You've done it! Now, I shall join you!
I've created the world's very first robot!
How may I serve you?

Once upon a time...
I've done it!
I've created the world's very first robot!
How may I serve you?
DRAW HERE!
"Build me a tower—A tower so tall that it disappears into the clouds and rain above!"
Yes, master.
You've done it! Now, I shall join you!
OH, NO! I forgot to ask them to build a door!
Drats!
And so, the robots were stuck in the tower... Forever.
Hello?
END

Look, Edward — there are robots in the tall tower! COOL!
DR. TINKERTON and the ROBOT
And maybe from the top of the tower we can see why it's raining!!!
AAAAAHHHHH!!
Quiet, Edward! It's only a small spider hanging from the ceiling!

Show the spider coming down from the ceiling by drawing him at the end of each string!

It'll take more than a little spider to scare me.
But this is no small spider—LOOK!
IT'S A MONSTER SPIDER!
POP
But it didn't look big until it was right next to us.
LET'S GET OUT OF HERE!

Add backgrounds to the panels below to change these tiny insects into GIANT CREATURES!

LET'S GET OUT OF HERE!
WHO GOES THERE?
Gasp
Who wakes me from my peaceful slumber?
The giant!
What messy hair he has!
MOM

The giant's hair is messy because he just woke up from a nap...
What do you look like when you wake up?
1. After a good night's sleep.
2. After taking a nap.
3. After getting **NO** sleep at all.

OH, NO!
We're trapped between a giant and a spider!
Webster, my pet!!!
Thank you for finding him!
Huh?

I'm so happy you found Webster!
What can I do for you, brave knight?
We're trying to get to the Tall Tower to stop the rain.
Hmmm... I have an idea.
Get in!!!

Have a safe flight!
Almost there.

Large panels are good for showing scenery!
Draw the kingdom below!

BOOM!
CRASH!
Oh, my!

Edward and the knight bumped their heads pretty hard. So hard, that they are dazed and confused.
Draw birds, stars, or scribbles to show they are loopy.

Are you all right?
Yeah.
Good thing I was wearing my helmet.
This must be the way to the top of the tower.
CAUTION
KEEP OUT!
OoOH, Spooky.

Draw what's hiding in the shadows!
WHAT COULD IT BE?
bats?
snakes?
spiders?

Let's go!
We'll make that rain stop in no time!
WHEW
This is tiring!
pant
pant
pant

OOF!
Wow, look at all this stuff...
Those robots **MUST** be in here some-where!
Look— there they are!

Weird. This one's head is missing. That can't be good.
I KNOW— let's finish it! Maybe it can help us stop the rain.
Yeah!
We can make its head with this stuff.

Draw your own robot heads using the parts below.

ROBOT PARTS

Just a few more bolts to tighten...
Almost there...
Tah-dahhhhhhhh!
EEP!
AH!
You're right—this looks a little scary.
Sorry, Edward.
BONG!
Frvt!
Bzzt!
How's this?
Better!
Here goes nothin'.

The more panels you use, the longer something takes. It took the knight four panels to complete the robot. Can you draw the knight completing the robot in just two panels?

How may I serve you?
Can you make it stop raining?
No, but I can shoot a laser from my head.
ZAP!
Yowza!
ZZZZZ ZAP!
What the—?!
ZAP!
ZZZ ZAP!
HELP!

Get 'im, Edward!
CLANG!
BOOM!
LOOK OUT! The roof is collapsing!
Oh, no—the door is blocked!
The only way to escape is to climb out!
Argh, it's still raining!

LOOK! I see what's causing the rain!
BOO, HOO, HOO!
No one ever tells me bed-time stories!
What if WE told you a story?
Would you stop crying then?
Sniff
Sniff
Yeah.
Sniff
And if you stop crying it will stop raining!
YAY!

I like adventure stories!
Well, we just went on an adventure through the castle.
There were wizards, monsters, giants...
...and of course, a brave knight and his trusty steed.
There was even a tiny side-kick!
Hey!
That sounds exciting!
It WAS! I bet we could make a story using those characters.
Oh, please do!
Okay, here we go:
Once upon a time...

Now it's your turn!
Use the blank panels on the following pages to make your own comic. Here are some cartooning tools you can use:
Comics are made up of PANELS.
A panel shows a moment in time.
The more panels you have, the longer something takes.
BACKGROUNDS
Create a sense of scale by adding back-grounds.
START
END
Comics are read from LEFT to RIGHT, TOP to BOTTOM.

WORD BALLOONS
show what a character is saying.
THOUGHT BALLOONS
show what a character is thinking.
The way a word balloon is shaped can change what it means.
SCREAM!
WHISPER
But the most important thing to keep in mind is to...
HAVE FUN!

Start your comic by using this large panel to show where it takes place.

Once upon a time...

THE END

Good evening, Moon.
Hello, Sun.
How was your day?
GREAT! I just read the most awesome story — it was a comic!
Cool, you'll have to tell me about it sometime.
Maybe tomorrow. Good night!

ISBN 978-0-545-31259-2

Published by Scholastic Inc., 557 Broadway, New York, NY 10012, by arrangement with First Second, an imprint of Roaring Brook Press, a division of Holtzbrinck Publishing Holdings Limited Partnership.

12 11 10 9 8 7 6 5 4 3 2 1 10 11 12 13 14 15/0

Printed in the U.S.A. 40

First Scholastic printing, October 2010

And they all made comics happily ever after.